More Mental Maths Tests

for ages 7–8

✓ **Ten complete Mental Maths timed tests, together with a pre-recorded CD**

✓ **Ideal practice for National Tests**

✓ **Bonus material includes record sheets and addition squares**

Introduction

Our Mental Maths Tests were originally devised to provide practice for the optional tests for Years 3, 4 and 5 taking place in May using the same test materials each year. The materials in this book provide practice for the type of questions that appear in those tests but also for other aspects of mathematics at the appropriate levels indicated by the National Numeracy Framework.

Many teachers have found that our tests provide a very useful structure for consolidation lessons. By working through the tests with the pupils, teachers can gain valuable insights into their pupils' levels of performance. At the same time the children are gaining experience of working in a test situation, listening to recorded questions that are timed in the same way as the 'real' test.

General instructions for the administration of the tests

To make these tests seem as realistic as possible children should have clear desks and only a pen or pencil to write with. They should not be supplied with paper for working out the answers.

Before starting each test the children should write their name and school in the spaces provided.

Inform the children that:

- they should work individually and should not talk at all during the test;

- there will be 15 questions altogether;

- they will be allowed 5 seconds to answer each of the first ten questions and 10 seconds for each of the next five questions;

- for some questions, some information will be provided on the test sheet;

- calculators or other equipment are not allowed;

- they should not rub out answers but, if they wish to change them, they can cross them out and write their new answers next to the incorrect ones;

- if they cannot do a question they should put a cross in the answer box.

Test 1

Before playing the test on the CD give each child a copy of the test and read out the following script:

> **Listen to the instructions carefully. I will answer any questions that you have after I have finished reading the instructions to you. Once the test starts you will not be able to ask any questions.**
>
> **The first question is a practice question. In the test there will then be fifteen questions.**
>
> **Each question has an answer box. Make sure that you only write the answer to the correct question in the box. Try to work out each answer in your head. You can make notes outside the answer box if this helps you but do not try to write out calculations because you will not have enough time. For some questions you will find important information already provided for you.**
>
> **Each question will be read out twice. Listen carefully then work out your answer. If you cannot do the question, just put a cross. If you make a mistake, do not rub out the wrong answer; cross it out and write the correct answer.**
>
> **Some questions are easy and some are more difficult. Do not worry if you find a question hard; just do your best. I hope that you enjoy the test.**

At this point, answer any questions that the children ask.

> **Now listen carefully to the practice question. You will hear the question twice, then you will have five seconds to work out and write down the answer.**
>
> *What is six add two?*
>
> *What is six add two?*

Allow the children five seconds to write the answer, then say:

> **Put your pencil down.**

Check that the children have written the answer to the practice question in the practice question answer box. Remind them that they cannot ask any more questions once the test is started. When you are ready, press start on your CD player.

When the test is finished ask the children to stop writing, then collect the test sheets. For ease of marking we have created a copy of the test paper with the answers entered in the appropriate boxes.

Questions for Test 1

For each of the first ten questions you have five seconds to work out and write down the answer.

1   What is the total of seven and six?

2   How many seconds are there in half a minute?

3   What number is half of twelve?

4   How many sides does a rectangle have?

5   Subtract three from eight.

6   What is six times three?

7   Look at your answer sheet. Draw a ring around the even number.

8   If I buy a sweet for sixteen pence, how much change will I have from twenty pence?

9   What number is double twenty?

10   What is ten times thirty?

For each of the next questions you have ten seconds to work out and write down the answer.

11   Look at your answer sheet. The jug has some water in it. How much water?

12   What is the sum of seventeen and nine?

13   How many minutes are there in two hours?

14   What number is ten less than three hundred and six?

15   Look at your answer sheet. Put a tick by the name of the shape.

Put your pencil down. The test is over.

Andrew Brodie: More Mental Maths Tests 7–8 © A & C Black

Test 1

First name _____   Last name _____

School _____

_____

Total marks

Practice question

Five-second questions

1

2 | seconds

3

4

5

6

7 | 5   11   26   29

8 | p | 16p   20p

9

10

Ten-second questions

11 | ml |

12 | | 17   9

13 | minutes | 2 hours

14 | | 306

15 | | pentagon

hexagon

octagon

triangle

Practice question

	8

Five-second questions

1	13

2	30 seconds

3	6

4	4

5	5

6	18

7	5 11 (26) 29

8	4p	16p 20p

9	40

10	300

Ten-second questions

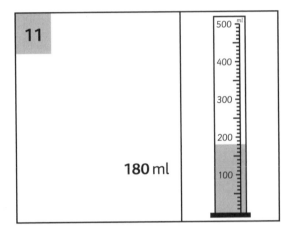

11	180 ml

12	26	17 9

13	120 minutes	2 hours

14	296	306

15		pentagon
		hexagon ✔
		octagon
		triangle

Test 2

Before playing the test on the CD give each child a copy of the test and read out the following script:

Listen to the instructions carefully. I will answer any questions that you have after I have finished reading the instructions to you. Once the test starts you will not be able to ask any questions.

The first question is a practice question. In the test there will then be fifteen questions.

Each question has an answer box. Make sure that you only write the answer to the correct question in the box. Try to work out each answer in your head. You can make notes outside the answer box if this helps you but do not try to write out calculations because you will not have enough time. For some questions you will find important information already provided for you.

Each question will be read out twice. Listen carefully then work out your answer. If you cannot do the question, just put a cross. If you make a mistake, do not rub out the wrong answer; cross it out and write the correct answer.

Some questions are easy and some are more difficult. Do not worry if you find a question hard; just do your best. I hope that you enjoy the test.

At this point, answer any questions that the children ask.

Now listen carefully to the practice question. You will hear the question twice, then you will have five seconds to work out and write down the answer..

What is seven take away three?

What is seven take away three

Allow the children five seconds to write the answer, then say:

Put your pencil down.

Check that the children have written the answer to the practice question in the practice question answer box. Remind them that they cannot ask any more questions once the test is started. When you are ready press start on your CD player.

When the test is finished ask the children to stop writing then collect the test sheets. For ease of marking we have created a copy of the test paper with the answers entered in the appropriate boxes.

For each of the first ten questions you have five seconds to work out and write down the answer.

1   How many weeks are there in a fortnight?

2   What is eight plus six?

3   What is twenty minus fifteen?

4   Round twenty-seven to the nearest ten.

5   What number is ten more than ninety-two?

6   Look at your answer sheet. Draw a ring around the odd number.

7   Write the next number in the sequence three, six, nine, twelve ...

8   Write this number in figures: two hundred and sixteen.

9   How many ten pence pieces are there in one pound?

10   Beth has a piece of wood that is half a metre long. How many centimetres long is her piece of wood?

For each of the next questions you have ten seconds to work out and write down the answer.

11   What is the total of six, seven and eight?

12   Look at your answer sheet. What fraction of the circle is shaded?

13   What is double sixteen?

14   Look at your answer sheet. What number does the tally represent?

15   If the thirty-first of January is a Sunday, what day is the first of February?

Put your pencil down. The test is over.

Andrew Brodie: More Mental Maths Tests 7–8 © A & C Black

First name _____   Last name _____

School _____

_____   **Total marks** [   ]

Practice question

[   ]

Five-second questions

1 [   ] weeks

2 [   ]

3 [   ]

4 [   ] 27

5 [   ] 92

6 25   8   14   32

7 3   6   9   12 [   ]

8 [   ] two hundred and sixteen

9 [   ]

10 [   ] cm | $\frac{1}{2}$ m

Ten-second questions

11 [   ] 6   7   8

12

13 [   ]

14 [   ] ЖЖ ЖЖ II

15 Sunday 31st January [   ]

Test 2 Answers

Practice question

4

Five-second questions

1	2

2	14

3	5

4	30	27

5	102	92

6	(25)	8	14	32

7	3 6 9 12	15

8	216
	two hundred and sixteen

9	10

10	50 cm	$\frac{1}{2}$ m

Ten-second questions

11	21	6 7 8

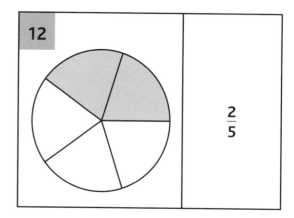

12		$\frac{2}{5}$

13	32

14	12	ⵜⵜⵜ ⵜⵜⵜ ‖

15	Sunday 31st January	Monday

Andrew Brodie: More Mental Maths Tests 7–8 © A & C Black

Test 3

Before playing the test on the CD give each child a copy of the test and read out the following script:

> **Listen to the instructions carefully. I will answer any questions that you have after I have finished reading the instructions to you. Once the test starts you will not be able to ask any questions.**
>
> **The first question is a practice question. In the test there will then be fifteen questions.**
>
> **Each question has an answer box. Make sure that you only write the answer to the correct question in the box. Try to work out each answer in your head. You can make notes outside the answer box if this helps you but do not try to write out calculations because you will not have enough time. For some questions you will find important information already provided for you.**
>
> **Each question will be read out twice. Listen carefully then work out your answer. If you cannot do the question, just put a cross. If you make a mistake, do not rub out the wrong answer; cross it out and write the correct answer.**
>
> **Some questions are easy and some are more difficult. Do not worry if you find a question hard; just do your best. I hope that you enjoy the test.**

At this point, answer any questions that the children ask.

> **Now listen carefully to the practice question. You will hear the question twice, then you will have five seconds to work out and write down the answer.**
>
> *What is six add three?*
>
> *What is six add three?*

Allow the children five seconds to write the answer, then say:

> **Put your pencil down.**

Check that the children have written the answer to the practice question in the practice question answer box. Remind them that they cannot ask any more questions once the test is started. When you are ready press start on your CD player.

When the test is finished ask the children to stop writing then collect the test sheets. For ease of marking we have created a copy of the test paper with the answers entered in the appropriate boxes.

Questions for Test 3

For each of the first ten questions you have five seconds to work out and write down the answer.

1   What is eight minus six?

2   Add four to eighteen.

3   How many months are there in one year?

4   Look at your answer sheet. Shade one quarter of the circle.

5   Forty add thirty.

6   What is six times four?

7   How much money is four twenty pence pieces?

8   What number is double twenty-five?

9   How many twos make eight?

10   What number is one less than five hundred?

For each of the next questions you have ten seconds to work out and write down the answer.

11   Look at your answer sheet. How much liquid is in the measuring cylinder?

12   How many days are there in a fortnight?

13   What number is half of twenty-six?

14   Look at your answer sheet. Put a tick by the name of the shape.

15   If I buy a cake for seventy-five pence how much change will I have from one pound?

Put your pencil down. The test is over.

Andrew Brodie: More Mental Maths Tests 7–8 © A & C Black

Test 3

First name _____   Last name _____

School _____

_____   **Total marks** [   ]

Practice question

[   ]

Five-second questions

1 [   ]

2 [   ]

3 [   ] months

4

5 [   ]

6 [   ]

7 [   ] p | 20p

8 [   ]

9 [   ]

10 [   ] 500

Ten-second questions

11
ml

12 [   ] days

13 [   ] 26

14
pentagon

hexagon

octagon

triangle

15 [   ] 75p

Practice question

	9

Five-second questions

1	2

2	22

3	12 months

4	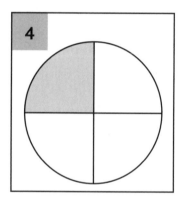

5	70

6	24

7	80p	20p

8	50

9	4

10	499	500

Ten-second questions

11	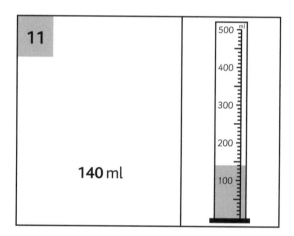 140 ml

12	14 days

13	13	26

14	pentagon hexagon octagon ✔ triangle

15	25p	75p

Test 4

Before playing the test on the CD give each child a copy of the test and read out the following script:

> **Listen to the instructions carefully. I will answer any questions that you have after I have finished reading the instructions to you. Once the test starts you will not be able to ask any questions.**
>
> **The first question is a practice question. In the test there will then be fifteen questions.**
>
> **Each question has an answer box. Make sure that you only write the answer to the correct question in the box. Try to work out each answer in your head. You can make notes outside the answer box if this helps you but do not try to write out calculations because you will not have enough time. For some questions you will find important information already provided for you.**
>
> **Each question will be read out twice. Listen carefully then work out your answer. If you cannot do the question, just put a cross. If you make a mistake, do not rub out the wrong answer; cross it out and write the correct answer.**
>
> **Some questions are easy and some are more difficult. Do not worry if you find a question hard; just do your best. I hope that you enjoy the test.**

At this point, answer any questions that the children ask.

> **Now listen carefully to the practice question. You will hear the question twice, then you will have five seconds to work out and write down the answer.**
>
> > ***What is seven add three?***
> >
> > ***What is seven add three?***

Allow the children five seconds to write the answer, then say:

> **Put your pencil down.**

Check that the children have written the answer to the practice question in the practice question answer box. Remind them that they cannot ask any more questions once the test is started. When you are ready, press start on your CD player.

When the test is finished ask the children to stop writing, then collect the test sheets. For ease of marking we have created a copy of the test paper with the answers entered in the appropriate boxes.

Questions for Test 4

For each of the first ten questions you have five seconds to work out and write down the answer.

1 What is ten times thirteen?

2 Add six to fifteen.

3 Write this number in figures: four hundred and twenty-seven.

4 What is double seven?

5 Which direction is opposite to North?

6 How many minutes are there in one hour?

7 What is four multiplied by seven?

8 Look at your answer sheet. Draw a ring around the odd number.

9 Look at your answer sheet. What fraction of the circle is shaded?

10 What is twenty minus twelve?

For each of the next questions you have ten seconds to work out and write down the answer.

11 Seventy-six subtract fifty-one.

12 Look at your answer sheet. What measurement is shown on the scales?

13 Jasdeep has forty pence. How much more does she need to make one pound?

14 What is double thirty-two?

15 How many days are there in three weeks?

Put your pencil down. The test is over.

Andrew Brodie: More Mental Maths Tests 7–8 © A & C Black

First name _____ Last name _____

School _____

_____

Total marks [   ]

Practice question

[   ]

Five-second questions

1 [   ]

2 [   ]

3 [four hundred and twenty-seven]

4 [   ]

5 [North]

6 [minutes | one hour]

7 [   ]

8 [32   16   48   61]

9

10 [20   12]

Ten-second questions

11 [76   51]

12 [kg |]

13 [   ]

14 [32]

15 [days | three weeks]

Test 4   Answers

Practice question

	10

Five-second questions

1	130

2	21

3	427
	four hundred and twenty-seven

4	14

5	South	North

6	60 minutes	one hour

7	28

8	32 16 48 (61)

9		$\dfrac{3}{4}$

10	8	20 12

Ten-second questions

11	25	76 51

12	3.5 kg or $3\frac{1}{2}$ kg	

13	60p

14	64	32

15	21 days	three weeks

Andrew Brodie: More Mental Maths Tests 7–8 © A & C Black

Test 5

Before playing the test on the CD give each child a copy of the test and read out the following script:

> **Listen to the instructions carefully. I will answer any questions that you have after I have finished reading the instructions to you. Once the test starts you will not be able to ask any questions.**
>
> **The first question is a practice question. In the test there will then be fifteen questions.**
>
> **Each question has an answer box. Make sure that you only write the answer to the correct question in the box. Try to work out each answer in your head. You can make notes outside the answer box if this helps you but do not try to write out calculations because you will not have enough time. For some questions you will find important information already provided for you.**
>
> **Each question will be read out twice. Listen carefully then work out your answer. If you cannot do the question, just put a cross. If you make a mistake, do not rub out the wrong answer; cross it out and write the correct answer.**
>
> **Some questions are easy and some are more difficult. Do not worry if you find a question hard; just do your best. I hope that you enjoy the test.**

At this point, answer any questions that the children ask.

> **Now listen carefully to the practice question. You will hear the question twice, then you will have five seconds to work out and write down the answer.**
>
> > *What is eight take away five?*
> >
> > *What is eight take away five?*

Allow the children five seconds to write the answer, then say:

> **Put your pencil down.**

Check that the children have written the answer to the practice question in the practice question answer box. Remind them that they cannot ask any more questions once the test is started. When you are ready, press start on your CD player.

When the test is finished ask the children to stop writing, then collect the test sheets. For ease of marking we have created a copy of the test paper with the answers entered in the appropriate boxes.

Questions for Test 5

For each of the first ten questions you have five seconds to work out and write down the answer.

1   What is the difference between nine and fourteen?

2   What is eight times three?

3   What number is one hundred more than two hundred and thirty-seven?

4   Round eighty-seven to the nearest ten.

5   Look at your answer sheet. What time does the clock show?

6   Add six to thirteen.

7   What is double nine?

8   A car has four wheels. How many wheels do five cars have?

9   Write this number in figures: seven hundred and ninety-six.

10   How much money is six two-pence pieces?

For each of the next questions you have ten seconds to work out and write down the answer.

11   What is thirty-four add twenty-one?

12   What is the total of ten, eleven and twelve?

13   How many seconds are there in two minutes?

14   Look at your answer sheet. What number does the tally represent?

15   Meg has fifty-five pence. How much more does she need to make one pound?

Put your pencil down. The test is over.

Andrew Brodie: More Mental Maths Tests 7–8 © A & C Black

Test 5

First name _____ Last name _____

School _____

_____

Total marks [   ]

Practice question

[   ]

Five-second questions

| 1 | | 9   14 |

| 2 | |

| 3 | | 237 |

| 4 | | 87 |

| 5 | | |

| 6 | |

| 7 | |

| 8 | |

| 9 | |
| seven hundred and ninety-six |

| 10 | |

Ten-second questions

| 11 | | 34   21 |

| 12 | | 10   11   12 |

| 13 | | seconds | two minutes |

| 14 | | 卌 卌 卌 I |

| 15 | | p | 55p |

Practice question

	3

8	**20**

Five-second questions

1	**5**	9	14

9	**796**
	seven hundred and ninety-six

2	**24**

10	**12p**

3	**337**	237

Ten-second questions

4	**90**	87	

11	**55**	34	21

5	
Half past two or 2.30	

12	**33**	10 11 12	

13	**120** seconds	two minutes

6	**19**

14	**16**	卌 卌 卌 I

7	**18**

15	**45p**	55p

Andrew Brodie: More Mental Maths Tests 7–8 © A & C Black

Test 6

Before playing the test on the CD give each child a copy of the test and read out the following script:

> Listen to the instructions carefully. I will answer any questions that you have after I have finished reading the instructions to you. Once the test starts you will not be able to ask any questions.
>
> The first question is a practice question. In the test there will then be fifteen questions.
>
> Each question has an answer box. Make sure that you only write the answer to the correct question in the box. Try to work out each answer in your head. You can make notes outside the answer box if this helps you but do not try to write out calculations because you will not have enough time. For some questions you will find important information already provided for you.
>
> Each question will be read out twice. Listen carefully then work out your answer. If you cannot do the question, just put a cross. If you make a mistake, do not rub out the wrong answer; cross it out and write the correct answer.
>
> Some questions are easy and some are more difficult. Do not worry if you find a question hard; just do your best. I hope that you enjoy the test.

At this point, answer any questions that the children ask.

> Now listen carefully to the practice question. You will hear the question twice, then you will have five seconds to work out and write down the answer.
>
> *What is five add three?*
>
> *What is five add three?*

Allow the children five seconds to write the answer, then say:

> **Put your pencil down.**

Check that the children have written the answer to the practice question in the practice question answer box. Remind them that they cannot ask any more questions once the test is started. When you are ready, press start on your CD player.

When the test is finished ask the children to stop writing, then collect the test sheets. For ease of marking we have created a copy of the test paper with the answers entered in the appropriate boxes.

Questions for Test 6

For each of the first ten questions you have five seconds to work out and write down the answer.

1. What is the difference between twelve and eight?

2. What number is one less than three hundred?

3. Multiply five by nine.

4. Add seven to eight.

5. What is the product of twenty-three and ten?

6. Write an odd number that comes between fifty and sixty.

7. How many metres are there in a kilometre?

8. Write the next number in this sequence: fifteen, twenty, twenty-five, thirty, ...

9. What is double eight?

10. Which direction is opposite to South?

For each of the next questions you have ten seconds to work out and write down the answer.

11. Ben has five twenty pence coins. How much money is this altogether?

12. The distance all round a square is eight centimetres. How long is one side?

13. Look at your answer sheet. The stool has three legs. How many legs would six stools have altogether?

14. What is forty-three plus twenty-five?

15. Tariq has a one-pound coin. He spends fifty-eight pence. How much change does he have?

Put your pencil down. The test is over.

Andrew Brodie: More Mental Maths Tests 7–8 © A & C Black

Test 6

First name _____ Last name _____

School _____

School _____

Total marks [ ]

Practice question

[ ][ ]

Five-second questions

| 1 | | 12   8 |

| 2 | | 300 |

| 3 | |

| 4 | |

| 5 | | 23 |

| 6 | |
| 50   60 | |

| 7 | metres | 1 kilometre |

| 8 | 15   20   25   30 | | [ ]

| 9 | | [ ]

| 10 | | South | [ ]

Ten-second questions

| 11 | | 20p | [ ]

| 12 | | 8 cm | [ ]

| 13 | | | [ ]

| 14 | | 43   25 | [ ]

| 15 | | 58p | [ ]

Practice question

	8

Five-second questions

1	4	12	8

2	299	300

3	45

4	15

5	230	23

6	51 or 53 or 55 or 57 or 59
	50 60

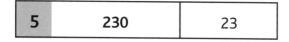

7	1000 metres	1 kilometre

8	15 20 25 30	35

9	16

10	North	South

Ten-second questions

11	£1	20p

12	2 cm	8 cm

13	18	

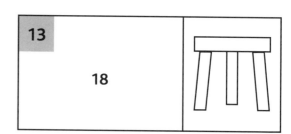

14	68	43 25

15	42p	58p

Andrew Brodie: More Mental Maths Tests 7–8 © A & C Black

Test 7

Before playing the test on the CD give each child a copy of the test and read out the following script:

> **Listen to the instructions carefully. I will answer any questions that you have after I have finished reading the instructions to you. Once the test starts you will not be able to ask any questions.**
>
> **The first question is a practice question. In the test there will then be fifteen questions.**
>
> **Each question has an answer box. Make sure that you only write the answer to the correct question in the box. Try to work out each answer in your head. You can make notes outside the answer box if this helps you but do not try to write out calculations because you will not have enough time. For some questions you will find important information already provided for you.**
>
> **Each question will be read out twice. Listen carefully then work out your answer. If you cannot do the question, just put a cross. If you make a mistake, do not rub out the wrong answer; cross it out and write the correct answer.**
>
> **Some questions are easy and some are more difficult. Do not worry if you find a question hard; just do your best. I hope that you enjoy the test.**

At this point, answer any questions that the children ask.

> **Now listen carefully to the practice question. You will hear the question twice, then you will have five seconds to work out and write down the answer.**
>
> *What is four add two?*
>
> *What is four add two?*

Allow the children five seconds to write the answer, then say:

> **Put your pencil down.**

Check that the children have written the answer to the practice question in the practice question answer box. Remind them that they cannot ask any more questions once the test is started. When you are ready, press start on your CD player.

When the test is finished ask the children to stop writing, then collect the test sheets. For ease of marking we have created a copy of the test paper with the answers entered in the appropriate boxes.

For each of the first ten questions you have five seconds to work out and write down the answer.

1 What is three plus seven?

2 What number is ten less than three hundred and four?

3 Round two hundred and forty-one to the nearest hundred.

4 Multiply two by nine.

5 Look at your answer sheet. What fraction of the rectangle is shaded?

6 How many centimetres are there in two metres?

7 Write this number in figures: eight hundred and two

8 What is the third month of the year?

9 What direction is opposite to West?

10 Take four from seventeen.

For each of the next questions you have ten seconds to work out and write down the answer.

11 Seth has a five pound note. He spends three pounds sixty pence. How much money does he have left?

12 What is three quarters of eight?

13 What is the total of ten, thirty and fifty?

14 What is eighty-five plus fifty?

15 The distance all round a square is twenty centimetres. How long is one side?

Put your pencil down. The test is over.

Andrew Brodie: More Mental Maths Tests 7–8 © A & C Black

Test 7

First name _____   Last name _____

School _____

_____   **Total marks** [   ]

Practice question

[   ]

Five-second questions

1 [   ]

2 [| 304]

3 [| 241]

4 [   ]

5

6 [cm | 2 m]

7 [| eight hundred and two]

8 [   ]

9 [| West]

10 [   ]

Ten-second questions

11 [£ | £3.60]

12 [| $\frac{3}{4}$ 8]

13 [| 10 30 50]

14 [| 85 50]

15 [cm | 20 cm]

Practice question

	6

Five-second questions

1	10

2	294	304

3	200	241

4	18

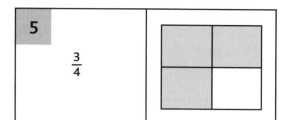

5	$\frac{3}{4}$

6	**200** cm	2 m

7	**802**
	eight hundred and two

8	March

9	East	West

10	13

Ten-second questions

11	£1.40	£3.60

12	6	$\frac{3}{4}$ 8

13	**90**	10 30 50

14	135	85 50

15	5 cm	20 cm

Test 8

Before playing the test on the CD give each child a copy of the test and read out the following script:

> **Listen to the instructions carefully. I will answer any questions that you have after I have finished reading the instructions to you. Once the test starts you will not be able to ask any questions.**
>
> **The first question is a practice question. In the test there will then be fifteen questions.**
>
> **Each question has an answer box. Make sure that you only write the answer to the correct question in the box. Try to work out each answer in your head. You can make notes outside the answer box if this helps you but do not try to write out calculations because you will not have enough time. For some questions you will find important information already provided for you.**
>
> **Each question will be read out twice. Listen carefully then work out your answer. If you cannot do the question, just put a cross. If you make a mistake, do not rub out the wrong answer; cross it out and write the correct answer.**
>
> **Some questions are easy and some are more difficult. Do not worry if you find a question hard; just do your best. I hope that you enjoy the test.**

At this point, answer any questions that the children ask.

> **Now listen carefully to the practice question. You will hear the question twice, then you will have five seconds to work out and write down the answer.**
>
> ### *What is eight add two?*
>
> ### *What is eight add two?*

Allow the children five seconds to write the answer, then say:

> **Put your pencil down.**

Check that the children have written the answer to the practice question in the practice question answer box. Remind them that they cannot ask any more questions once the test is started. When you are ready, press start on your CD player.

When the test is finished ask the children to stop writing, then collect the test sheets. For ease of marking we have created a copy of the test paper with the answers entered in the appropriate boxes.

Questions for Test 8

For each of the first ten questions you have five seconds to work out and write down the answer.

1   What is six add five?

2   How many years are there in a century?

3   How many seconds are there in half a minute?

4   Multiply twenty-five by ten.

5   Thirteen subtract five.

6   How many grams are there in half a kilogram?

7   Add seven to twenty-five.

8   Round ninety-three to the nearest ten.

9   What is five times six?

10   What month comes after May?

For each of the next questions you have ten seconds to work out and write down the answer.

11   Look at the hexagon on your answer sheet. How many sides would four of these hexagons have altogether?

12   What is double eighteen?

13   What is one hundred and twenty minus forty?

14   If I spend one pound fifty pence what change will I have from a five pound note?

15   Look at your answer sheet. What fraction of the circle is shaded?

Put your pencil down. The test is over.

Andrew Brodie: More Mental Maths Tests 7–8 © A & C Black

Test 8

First name _____   Last name _____

School _____

_____   **Total marks** [   ]

Practice question

[   ]

Five-second questions

1 [   ]

2 [   ] years

3 [   ] seconds | half a minute

4 [   ] | 25

5 [   ]

6 [   ] g | $\frac{1}{2}$ kilogram

7 [   ]

8 [   ] | 93

9 [   ]

10 [   ] | May

Ten-second questions

11 [   ]

12 [   ]

13 [   ] | 120   40

14 £ [   ] | £1.50

15 [   ]

Practice question

	10

Five-second questions

1	11

2	100 years

3	30 seconds	half a minute

4	250	25

5	8

6	500 g	$\frac{1}{2}$ kilogram

7	32

8	90	93

9	30

10	June	May

Ten-second questions

11	24

12	36

13	80	120 40

14	£3.50	£1.50

15	$\frac{7}{10}$

Andrew Brodie: More Mental Maths Tests 7–8 © A & C Black

Test 9

Before playing the test on the CD give each child a copy of the test and read out the following script:

> **Listen to the instructions carefully. I will answer any questions that you have after I have finished reading the instructions to you. Once the test starts you will not be able to ask any questions.**
>
> **The first question is a practice question. In the test there will then be fifteen questions.**
>
> **Each question has an answer box. Make sure that you only write the answer to the correct question in the box. Try to work out each answer in your head. You can make notes outside the answer box if this helps you but do not try to write out calculations because you will not have enough time. For some questions you will find important information already provided for you.**
>
> **Each question will be read out twice. Listen carefully then work out your answer. If you cannot do the question, just put a cross. If you make a mistake, do not rub out the wrong answer; cross it out and write the correct answer.**
>
> **Some questions are easy and some are more difficult. Do not worry if you find a question hard; just do your best. I hope that you enjoy the test.**

At this point, answer any questions that the children ask.

> **Now listen carefully to the practice question. You will hear the question twice, then you will have five seconds to work out and write down the answer.**
>
> > *What is six take away three?*
> >
> > *What is six take away three?*

Allow the children five seconds to write the answer, then say:

> **Put your pencil down.**

Check that the children have written the answer to the practice question in the practice question answer box. Remind them that they cannot ask any more questions once the test is started. When you are ready, press start on your CD player.

When the test is finished ask the children to stop writing, then collect the test sheets. For ease of marking we have created a copy of the test paper with the answers entered in the appropriate boxes.

Questions for Test 9

For each of the first ten questions you have five seconds to work out and write down the answer.

1   What is twelve plus four?

2   What number is one hundred less than seven hundred and nineteen?

3   Subtract five from eleven.

4   How many centimetres are there in one quarter of a metre?

5   What is the product of seven and three?

6   Three children share fifteen sweets equally. How many sweets does each child have?

7   Multiply seventeen by ten.

8   What is double six?

9   Write an even number that is between sixty-one and seventy-one.

10   What month comes before April?

For each of the next questions you have ten seconds to work out and write down the answer.

11   Look at your answer sheet. Draw a ring around the biggest number.

12   Look at your answer sheet. What measurement is shown on the scales?

13   I think of a number. I subtract seven. The answer is eight. What was the number I thought of?

14   Jess has seventy-five pence then her granddad gives her sixty pence more. How much has she got now?

15   Holly has two pieces of wood that are both eighty centimetres long. She joins them end to end. What length of wood has she got altogether?

Put your pencil down. The test is over.

Andrew Brodie: More Mental Maths Tests 7–8 © A & C Black

First name _____   Last name _____

School _____

_____

Total marks [   ]

Practice question

[   ]

Five-second questions

| 1 | |

| 2 | | 719 |

| 3 | |

| 4 | | cm | $\frac{1}{4}$ m |

| 5 | |

| 6 | | sweets | 15 sweets |

| 7 | | 17 |

| 8 | |

| 9 | |
| | 61   71 |

| 10 | | April |

Ten-second questions

| 11 | 467   764   647   674 |

| 12 | kg |

| 13 | | 7   8 |

| 14 | | 75p |

| 15 | | 80 cm |

Practice question

	3

Five-second questions

1	16

2	619	719

3	6

4	25 cm	$\frac{1}{4}$ m

5	21

6	5 sweets	15 sweets

7	170	17

8	12

9	62 or 64 or 66 or 68 or 70
	61 71

10	March	April

Ten-second questions

11	467	(764)	647	674

12	2.5 kg or $2\frac{1}{2}$ kg	

13	15	7 8

14	£1.35	75p

15	1.6 m or 160 cm	80 cm

Andrew Brodie: More Mental Maths Tests 7–8 © A & C Black

Test 10

Before playing the test on the CD give each child a copy of the test and read out the following script:

Listen to the instructions carefully. I will answer any questions that you have after I have finished reading the instructions to you. Once the test starts you will not be able to ask any questions.

The first question is a practice question. In the test there will then be fifteen questions.

Each question has an answer box. Make sure that you only write the answer to the correct question in the box. Try to work out each answer in your head. You can make notes outside the answer box if this helps you but do not try to write out calculations because you will not have enough time. For some questions you will find important information already provided for you.

Each question will be read out twice. Listen carefully then work out your answer. If you cannot do the question, just put a cross. If you make a mistake, do not rub out the wrong answer; cross it out and write the correct answer.

Some questions are easy and some are more difficult. Do not worry if you find a question hard; just do your best. I hope that you enjoy the test.

At this point, answer any questions that the children ask.

Now listen carefully to the practice question. You will hear the question twice, then you will have five seconds to work out and write down the answer.

What is five add four?

What is five add four?

Allow the children five seconds to write the answer, then say:

Put your pencil down.

Check that the children have written the answer to the practice question in the practice question answer box. Remind them that they cannot ask any more questions once the test is started. When you are ready, press start on your CD player.

When the test is finished ask the children to stop writing, then collect the test sheets. For ease of marking we have created a copy of the test paper with the answers entered in the appropriate boxes.

Questions for Test 10

For each of the first ten questions you have five seconds to work out and write down the answer.

1   Add nine and eight.

2   How much more is eighteen than twelve?

3   What is the product of eight and six?

4   Divide thirty-two by four.

5   What is ten times fourteen?

6   What number is ten more than eight hundred and ninety-seven?

7   Round seventy-eight to the nearest ten.

8   How many centimetres are there in three and a half metres?

9   What is fifty-seven plus eight?

10   Look at your answer sheet. What time does the clock show?

For each of the next questions you have ten seconds to work out and write down the answer.

11   What number is half of thirty-eight?

12   Write the next number in this sequence: sixty-five, fifty-five, forty-five, thirty-five, ...

13   Add eighty to one hundred and seventy.

14   Jess buys two pens for seventy-five pence each. How much does she spend?

15   Look at your test sheet. Shade three fifths of the circle.

Put your pencil down. The test is over.

Andrew Brodie: More Mental Maths Tests 7–8 © A & C Black

Test 10

First name _____   Last name _____

School _____

_____

Total marks ☐

Practice question

☐ [ ]

Five-second questions

1	

2		18 12

3	

4		32

5	

6		897

7		78

8	cm	$3\frac{1}{2}$ m

9		57

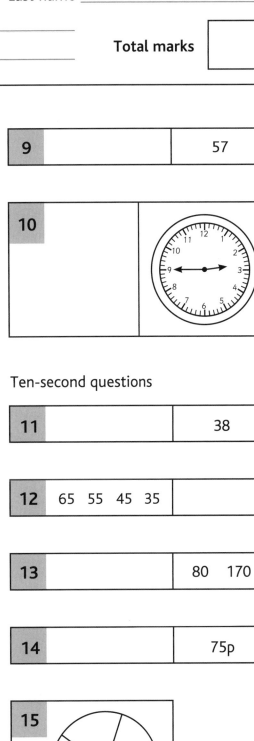

10	

Ten-second questions

11		38

12	65 55 45 35	

13		80 170

14		75p

15	

Practice question

	9

Five-second questions

1	17

2	6	18 12

3	48

4	8	32

5	140

6	907	897

7	80	78

8	350 cm	$3\frac{1}{2}$ m

9	65	57

10	2.45 or quarter to three	

Ten-second questions

11	19	38

12	65 55 45 35	25

13	250	80 170

14	£1.50 or 150p	75p

15	

Pupil record sheet

You may wish to record your pupils' scores as they complete each test.

Page 44 consists of a record sheet on which you can enter the pupils' names down the left hand column and the dates of the tests along the top. On page 45 there is a graph for recording the scores for each individual pupil. By photocopying this sheet for every member of the class you can monitor each individual's progress from test to test.

It is worth observing where the pupils are making errors. Errors may occur on particular types of questions, perhaps where certain vocabulary is used. Is there a pattern to their problems?

You may also find that some pupils find the time restrictions challenging. Do they find the five-second questions more difficult, for example, simply due to the speed with which they have to answer?

Where patterns do emerge you will be able to target your teaching to address the pupils' needs. You should then find improvements as the pupils work through the set of tests.

Pages 46 to 48 provide some extra mental arithmetic practice.

Pupil Record Sheet

Class _____

Test number:	1	2	3	4	5	6	7	8	9	10
Date:										
Name:										

Andrew Brodie: More Mental Maths Tests 7–8 © A & C Black

Pupil Progress Graph

Name _____

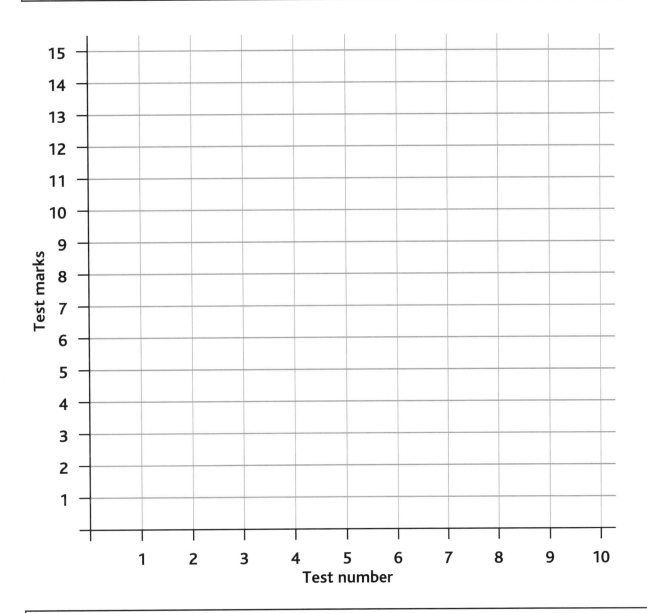

Comments, including any particular areas of difficulty

Mental Maths Puzzles

The puzzles below provide practice of addition and subtraction facts as well as of logical thinking. More puzzles like these, together with harder versions, can be found in Maths Mindstretchers for Ages 7–9.

Name _____   Date _____

Look carefully at the puzzle. It has a target number of 7.

You need to write some numbers to make a subtraction with an answer of 7 and an addition with an answer of 7.

Here are the numbers you must use:
2 3 4 9

Now try this one.
Target number: 14.

Numbers to use:
3 5 9 17

Now try this one.
Target number: 9.

Numbers to use:
3 4 5 12

Now try this one.
Target number: 15.

Numbers to use:
3 4 12 19

Mental Maths Puzzles

The puzzles below provide practice of addition and subtraction facts as well as of logical thinking. They are more difficult than those on page 46. More puzzles like these, together with harder versions, can be found in Maths Mindstretchers for Ages 7–9.

Name _____   Date _____

Look carefully at the puzzle. You need to find the target number that goes in the middle and you need to write numbers in the correct places to make a subtraction sentence and an addition sentence.

Here are the numbers you must use:
4 5 7 12 16

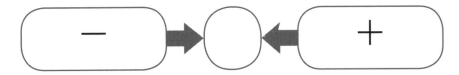

Here is another puzzle. You need to find the target number and the numbers to make the subtraction sentence and the addition sentence.

The numbers you must
use are:
3 4 4 8 11

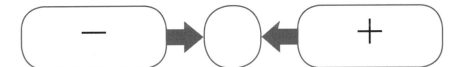

Now try this one.

The numbers you must
use are:
2 3 7 9 12

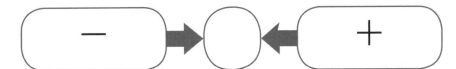

Now try this one.

The numbers you must
use are:
5 7 8 13 20

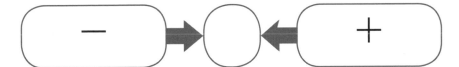

Mental Maths Puzzles

The puzzles below provide practice of addition and multiplication facts as well as of logical thinking. They are more difficult than those on page 47. More puzzles like these, together with harder versions, can be found in Maths Mindstretchers for Ages 7–9.

Name _____ Date _____

Look carefully at the puzzle. You need to find the target number that goes in the middle and you need to write numbers in the correct places to make an addition sentence and a multiplication sentence.

Here are the numbers you must use:
3 5 6 9 15

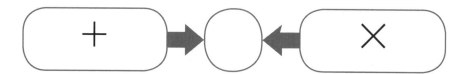

Here is another puzzle. You need to find the target number and the numbers to make the addition sentence and the multiplication sentence.

The numbers you must use are:
3 6 8 18 24

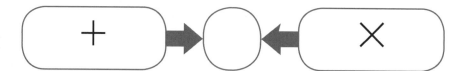

Now try this one.

The numbers you must use are:
4 5 6 26 30

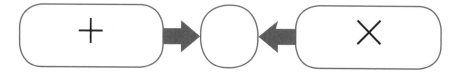

Now try this one.

The numbers you must use are:
4 7 9 19 28

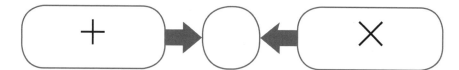